THIS BOOK BELONGS TO:

Golden Age Press

VISIT US ONLINE:
WWW.GOLDENAGEPRESS.COM

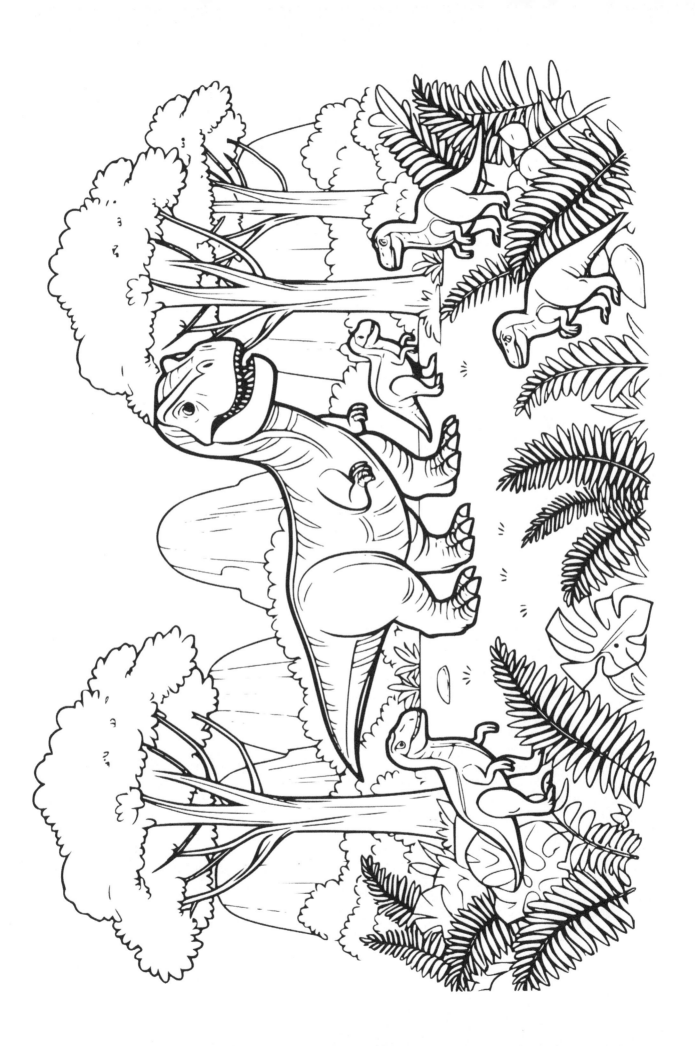

Check out all our fun coloring books, activity books, back to school notebooks and more!

www.goldenagepress.com

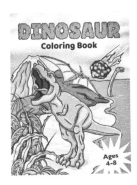    

Made in United States
Orlando, FL
07 April 2024

45539046R00057